Harry's Bee

Harry's

Bee

by Peter Campbell

THE BOBBS-MERRILL COMPANY, INC.

Indianapolis   New York

The Bobbs-Merrill Company, Inc. A Subsidiary of Howard W. Sams & Co., Inc., Publishers
Indianapolis Kansas City New York. First published by Methuen & Co., Ltd., in Great Britain in 1969.
Copyright © 1969 by Peter Campbell. Printed in the United States of America.

Harry's Bee

Once upon a time there was a man called
Harry who grew the biggest rose in England.
It was as big as your head.

One day, when Harry went to see how it was growing,
he heard a loud buzzing sound.

He looked up and saw a huge bee come buzzing down
to land on the rose.

It was the biggest bee in England.

He dived into Harry's rose and came out again
half an hour later.

   "You don't often find a rose as good as that," he said.

   "No," said Harry. "But then, that's the biggest rose
in England."

The Bee came back every day. When he could get nothing
more from the rose, Harry took him into the kitchen
to get some honey from a pot. He and the Bee often
talked together and both agreed they had never met
anyone else they liked as well as they liked each other.

So Harry made a bee-basket and the two of them set off
together to see the world.

They travelled by train. When the
guard came, Harry asked if he needed
a ticket for his bee. The guard
said, "What?" Then Harry opened the
basket. The guard went very white
and didn't ask again – he went out
very fast. The other passengers
went out too – and shut the door.

So Harry and the Bee
always had plenty of room,
and seats by the window.

As they went from town to town, the Bee got to think himself
more and more important. He saw so many people at the railway
stations and in the streets get out of his way, he thought he
must be very grand. So he said to Harry, "As I'm the biggest
bee in England, it's time I was seen by the chief bee-keeper."

Harry said there wasn't a chief bee-keeper. The Bee said
the Prime Minister would do instead.

Harry said he'd rather not, but the Bee buzzed very loudly
and wouldn't go back into his basket until Harry promised to
take him. So he did.

He took his bee-basket to the Prime Minister's house and knocked.
The man who answered the door was very polite, but said there was
no time for visitors that day and they should try the Ministry
of Food and Fish. The Bee buzzed angrily, but Harry put him
back in his basket and the man shut the door.

The man at the Ministry of Food and Fish said honey was
more their line than bees, but that if they cared to write,
the Minister might see them another day. This too made
the Bee very angry. He flew out of his bee-basket and
buzzed loudly at the man. The man went pale and told
Harry to keep his bee on a leash. So Harry went out.

The Bee was furious. People kept looking at the basket,
wondering what was making the awful noise.

Harry was dejected. He went to a park and found a
bench to sit on.

While he was there, a boy came and sat down beside him.

"What's in that basket?" he asked.

"The biggest bee in England," said Harry.

"Can I see?" said the boy.

"He's cross," said Harry. "It's at your own risk."

The boy said that was all right, so Harry showed him the Bee.

"That's certainly a fine large bee," said the boy. "I've never seen a bigger one, not even in the Natural History Museum."

"What's that?" asked Harry.

"It's where they know about all the animals and insects in the world," said the boy.

"Then it's time they saw the biggest bee in England," said
the Bee, and asked the boy to lead the way. He did.
He took them to the main entrance. The man
there asked what Harry had in his basket.
"The biggest bee in England," said Harry.

The man didn't turn pale.
He asked if he could look.
When he saw the Bee, he
was delighted.

"The Keeper will want
to see you," he said, and
with the Bee buzzing overhead, he led the way.

When the Keeper saw the Bee, he went pink with pleasure.

"What a magnificent fellow," he said. "The Director will want to see you."

So they went on, the Bee again buzzing proudly overhead, till they came to the Director's office.

The Director stopped his work when he saw the Bee.
   "Whose is that?" he asked.
   "He's a friend of mine," said Harry. "He's the
biggest bee in England."
   The Director took a tape measure. He marked out
the length of the Bee on the wall. He turned to the Bee.

"You are not," he said, "the biggest bee in England."
The Bee started to mutter and buzz angrily, but the
Director went on. He said, "You are the biggest
bee in the World."

The Bee was delighted. He sang to them as he flew round
and round the room, then took a cup of tea and went back
into his basket.

When Harry and the Bee went home, they took a letter from the
Director saying that the Bee is the biggest in the World. They
live very happily together, and Harry still grows roses.

Every summer the Bee flies up to the Natural History Museum, where the Director marks his length on the wall. He is getting bigger every year.

Watch out for him!

ABOUT THE AUTHOR

PETER CAMPBELL was born and educated in Wellington, New Zealand, where he studied typography and printing. After working briefly for the New Zealand Department of Education, he moved to England in 1960 where he now works for BBC Publications. He is married and has two young children, and, like Harry, he enjoys gardening.